# Maths
## made easy

### Key Stage 2 lower
### ages 7-9
### Fractions

**Author**
Peter Gash

**Consultant**
David Clemson

LONDON • NEW YORK • SYDNEY • DELHI

# Halves of numbers

When you divide a number into halves, you share it equally between two.

One half is 3 spots.

Draw a ring to show one half of each set of spots. Then write the answers.

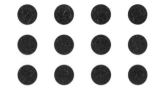

One half is ☐ spots.

One half is ☐ spots.

One half is ☐ spots.

One half is ☐ spots.

One half is ☐ spots.

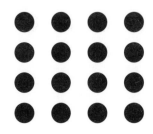

One half is ☐ spots.

# Halves of numbers

Draw a ring to show one half of each set of spots. Then write the answers.

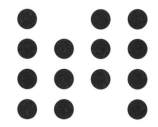

One half is ☐ spots.

One half is ☐ spots.

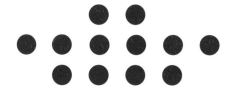

One half is ☐ spots.

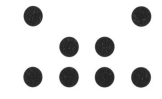

One half is ☐ spots.

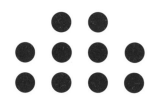

One half is ☐ spots.

One half is ☐ spots.

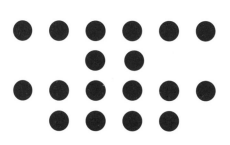

One half is ☐ spots.

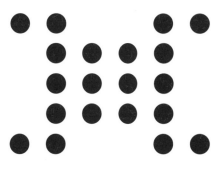

One half is ☐ spots.

# Halves of shapes

You can divide shapes into halves by drawing a line. Sometimes a shape can be divided in different ways.

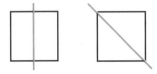

Draw a line to divide these shapes into halves in different ways. Then shade one half of each shape.

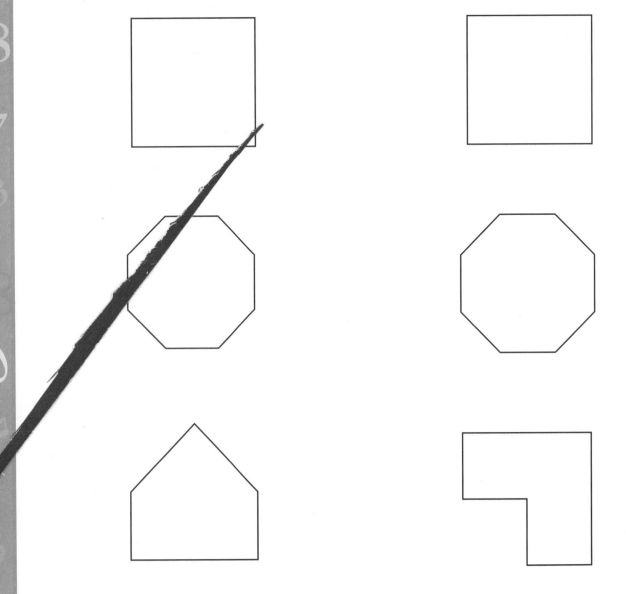

# Quarters of numbers

When you divide a number into quarters, you share it equally between four.

One quarter is 1 spot.

Draw lines to divide each set of spots into quarters. Then write the answers.

One quarter is ☐ spots.

One quarter is ☐ spots.

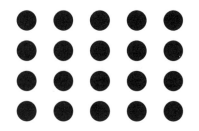

One quarter is ☐ spots.

One quarter is ☐ spots.

Write the answers.

One quarter of 4 is ☐

One quarter of 24 is ☐

One quarter of 40 is ☐

One quarter of 80 is ☐

# Quarters of shapes

You can divide shapes into quarters by drawing lines. Sometimes a shape can be divided in different ways.

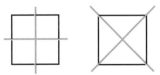

Draw lines to divide these shapes into quarters in different ways. Then shade one quarter of each shape.

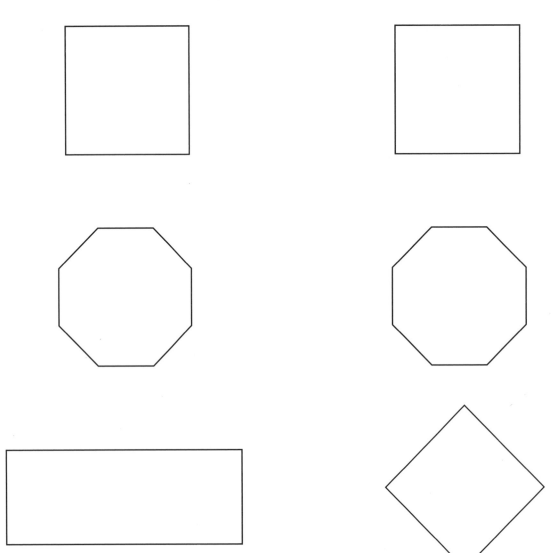

# Thirds of numbers

When you divide a number into thirds, you share it equally between three. Each part is called one third.
One third of 6 is 2, and two thirds of 6 is 4.

Draw a ring to show thirds of each set of balls. Then write the answers.

One third is ☐ balls.

Two thirds is ☐ balls.

One third is ☐ balls.

Two thirds is ☐ balls.

One third is ☐ balls.

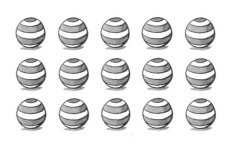

Two thirds is ☐ balls.

# Thirds of shapes

Draw lines to divide these shapes into thirds.

Shade one third of the shape.     Shade two thirds of the shape.

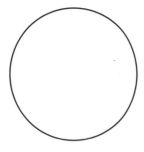     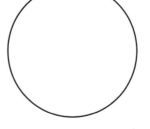

Shade one third of the shape.     Shade two thirds of the shape.

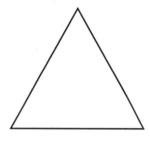     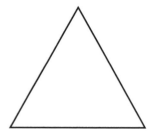

Shade one third of the shape.     Shade two thirds of the shape.

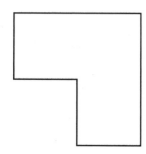     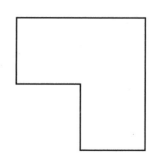

# Fifths of numbers

When you divide a number into fifths, you share it equally between five. Each part is called one fifth.
One fifth of 10 is 2, two fifths is 4, and so on.

Draw a ring to show fifths of each set of balls. Then write the answers.

One fifth is ☐ balls.

Two fifths is ☐ balls.

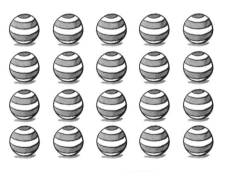

One fifth is ☐ balls.

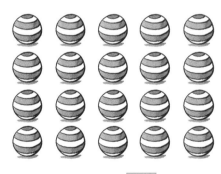

Two fifths is ☐ balls.

One fifth is ☐ balls.

Two fifths is ☐ balls.

# Fifths of shapes

Draw lines to divide these shapes into fifths.

Shade one fifth of the shape.

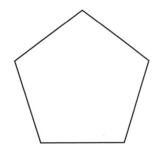

Shade two fifths of the shape.

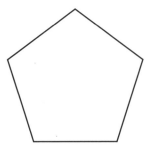

Shade three fifths of the shape.

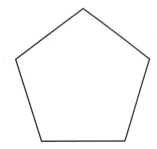

Shade four fifths of the shape.

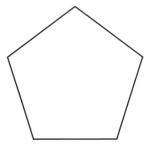

Shade one fifth of the shape.

Shade three fifths of the shape.

# Halves

When you divide something into halves, you share it equally between two.

Each part, or fraction, is called one half. You can also write it as ½.

Shade the squares to match the fractions. Write the answers.

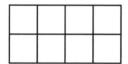

½ of 8 is ☐

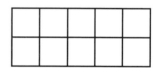

½ of 10 is ☐

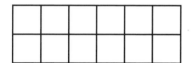

½ of 12 is ☐

½ of 6 is ☐

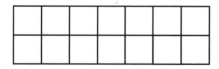

½ of 14 is ☐

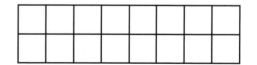

½ of 16 is ☐

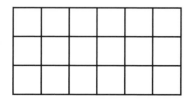

½ of 18 is ☐

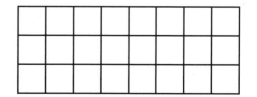

½ of 24 is ☐

# Quarters

When you divide something into quarters, you share it equally between four.

Each part, or fraction, is called one quarter. You can also write it as ¼.

Two parts are two quarters or ²⁄₄.
Three parts are three quarters or ³⁄₄.

Write the fractions for the shaded squares.

Shade the squares to show the fractions.

¼

³⁄₄

²⁄₄

⁴⁄₄

# Half of one half

One quarter is half of one half. For example:

4 is half of 8.

2 is half of one half of 8.

Therefore, 2 is one quarter of 8.

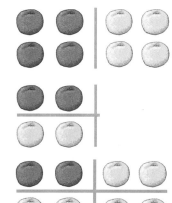

First find half of the number. Then divide the half in half to find one quarter.

Half of 8 is ☐

One quarter of 8 is ☐

Half of 16 is ☐

One quarter of 16 is ☐

Half of 20 is ☐

One quarter of 20 is ☐

Half of 24 is ☐

One quarter of 24 is ☐

# Half of one half

First find one half of these numbers and then one quarter.

|  | Half | Quarter |
|---|---|---|
| 4 | | |
| 8 | | |
| 12 | | |
| 16 | | |
| 20 | | |
| 24 | | |
| 28 | | |
| 32 | | |
| 36 | | |
| 40 | | |

# Quarters of shapes

Write the fractions for the shaded shapes.

# Thirds

When you divide something into thirds, you share it equally between three.

Each part, or fraction, is called one third. You can also write it as $\frac{1}{3}$.

Two parts are two thirds or $\frac{2}{3}$.

Write the fractions for the shaded squares.

Shade the squares to show the fractions.

$\frac{1}{3}$

$\frac{2}{3}$

$\frac{2}{3}$

$\frac{3}{3}$

# Answer Section

## Key Stage 2 lower
## Ages 7–9
## Fractions

As your child finishes each page, check the answers together. Your child may like to stick a gold star at the top of each completed page as well as on the progress chart at the beginning of the book.

---

## Halves of numbers

When you divide a number into halves, you share it equally between two.

One half is 3 spots.

Draw a ring to show one half of each set of spots. Then write the answers.

One half is **6** spots.

One half is **4** spots.

One half is **5** spots.

One half is **3** spots.

One half is **7** spots.

One half is **8** spots.

---

## Halves of numbers

Draw a ring to show one half of each set of spots. Then write the answers.

One half is **7** spots.

One half is **4** spots.

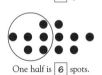
One half is **6** spots.

One half is **4** spots.

One half is **5** spots.

One half is **3** spots.

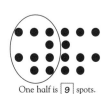
One half is **9** spots.

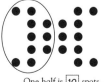
One half is **10** spots.

---

## Halves of shapes

You can divide shapes into halves by drawing a line. Sometimes a shape can be divided in different ways.

Draw a line to divide these shapes into halves in different ways. Then shade one half of each shape.

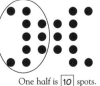

Answers may vary

# Quarters of numbers

When you divide a number into quarters, you share it equally between four.

One quarter is 1 spot.

Draw lines to divide each set of spots into quarters. Then write the answers.

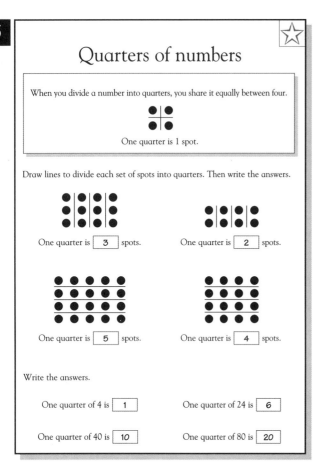

One quarter is 3 spots.

One quarter is 2 spots.

One quarter is 5 spots.

One quarter is 4 spots.

Write the answers.

One quarter of 4 is 1

One quarter of 24 is 6

One quarter of 40 is 10

One quarter of 80 is 20

# Quarters of shapes

You can divide shapes into quarters by drawing lines. Sometimes a shape can be divided in different ways.

Draw lines to divide these shapes into quarters in different ways. Then shade one quarter of each shape.

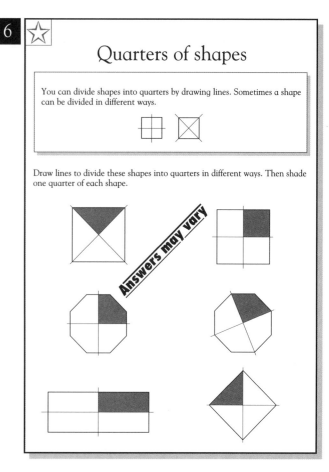

Answers may vary

# Thirds of numbers

When you divide a number into thirds, you share it equally between three. Each part is called one third.
One third of 6 is 2, and two thirds of 6 is 4.

Draw a ring to show thirds of each set of balls. Then write the answers.

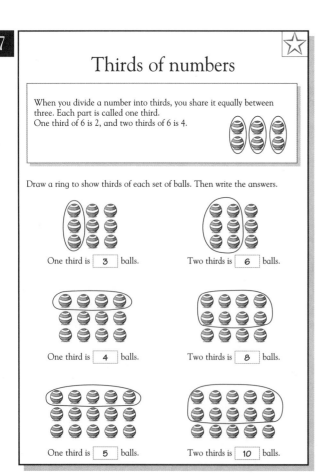

One third is 3 balls.

Two thirds is 6 balls.

One third is 4 balls.

Two thirds is 8 balls.

One third is 5 balls.

Two thirds is 10 balls.

# Thirds of shapes

Draw lines to divide these shapes into thirds.

Shade one third of the shape.

Shade two thirds of the shape.

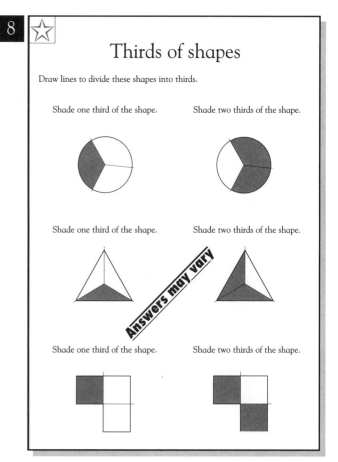

Shade one third of the shape.

Shade two thirds of the shape.

Answers may vary

Shade one third of the shape.

Shade two thirds of the shape.

**9**

# Fifths of numbers

When you divide a number into fifths, you share it equally between five.
Each part is called one fifth.
One fifth of 10 is 2, two fifths is 4, and so on.

Draw a ring to show fifths of each set of balls. Then write the answers.

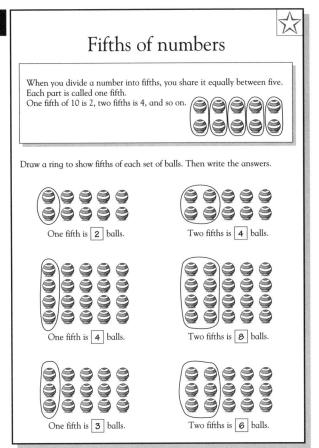

One fifth is [2] balls.          Two fifths is [4] balls.

One fifth is [4] balls.          Two fifths is [8] balls.

One fifth is [3] balls.          Two fifths is [6] balls.

**10**

# Fifths of shapes

Draw lines to divide these shapes into fifths.

Shade one fifth of the shape.          Shade two fifths of the shape.

Shade three fifths of the shape.          Shade four fifths of the shape.

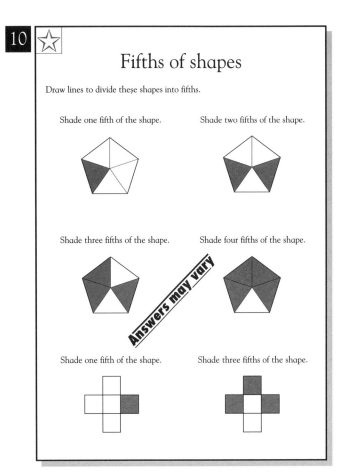

Answers may vary

Shade one fifth of the shape.          Shade three fifths of the shape.

**11**

# Halves

When you divide something into halves, you share it equally between two.

Each part, or fraction, is called one half.
You can also write it as $\frac{1}{2}$.

Shade the squares to match the fractions. Write the answers.

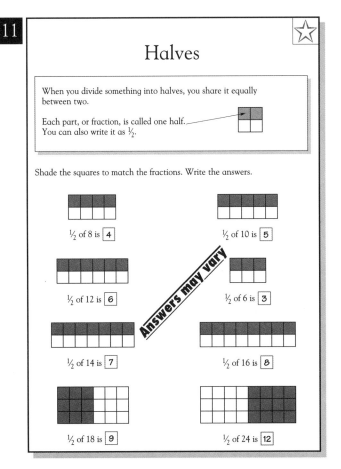

Answers may vary

$\frac{1}{2}$ of 8 is [4]          $\frac{1}{2}$ of 10 is [5]

$\frac{1}{2}$ of 12 is [6]          $\frac{1}{2}$ of 6 is [3]

$\frac{1}{2}$ of 14 is [7]          $\frac{1}{2}$ of 16 is [8]

$\frac{1}{2}$ of 18 is [9]          $\frac{1}{2}$ of 24 is [12]

**12**

# Quarters

When you divide something into quarters, you share it equally between four.

Each part, or fraction, is called one quarter.
You can also write it as $\frac{1}{4}$.

Two parts are two quarters or $\frac{2}{4}$.
Three parts are three quarters or $\frac{3}{4}$.

Write the fractions for the shaded squares.

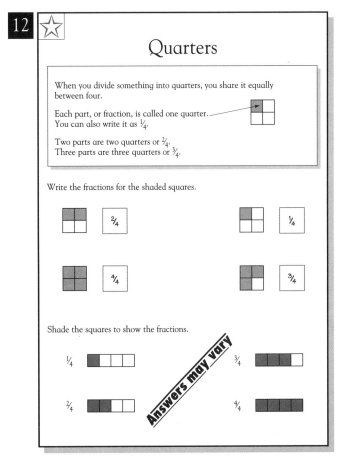

$\frac{2}{4}$          $\frac{1}{4}$

$\frac{4}{4}$          $\frac{3}{4}$

Shade the squares to show the fractions.

$\frac{1}{4}$          $\frac{3}{4}$

$\frac{2}{4}$          $\frac{4}{4}$

Answers may vary

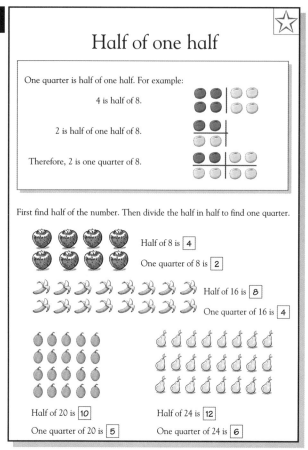

**13**

# Half of one half

One quarter is half of one half. For example:

4 is half of 8.

2 is half of one half of 8.

Therefore, 2 is one quarter of 8.

First find half of the number. Then divide the half in half to find one quarter.

Half of 8 is 4

One quarter of 8 is 2

Half of 16 is 8

One quarter of 16 is 4

Half of 20 is 10

One quarter of 20 is 5

Half of 24 is 12

One quarter of 24 is 6

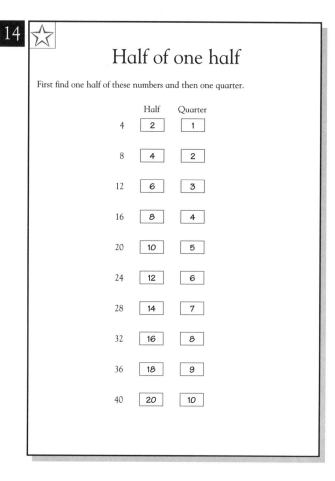

**14**

# Half of one half

First find one half of these numbers and then one quarter.

| | Half | Quarter |
|---|---|---|
| 4 | 2 | 1 |
| 8 | 4 | 2 |
| 12 | 6 | 3 |
| 16 | 8 | 4 |
| 20 | 10 | 5 |
| 24 | 12 | 6 |
| 28 | 14 | 7 |
| 32 | 16 | 8 |
| 36 | 18 | 9 |
| 40 | 20 | 10 |

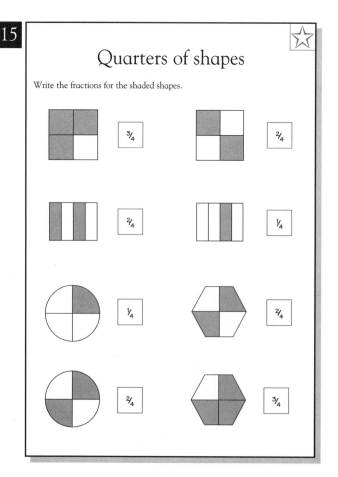

**15**

# Quarters of shapes

Write the fractions for the shaded shapes.

¾

²⁄₄

²⁄₄

¼

¼

²⁄₄

²⁄₄

¾

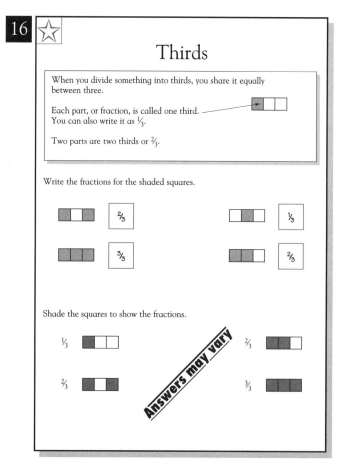

**16**

# Thirds

When you divide something into thirds, you share it equally between three.

Each part, or fraction, is called one third.
You can also write it as ⅓.

Two parts are two thirds or ⅔.

Write the fractions for the shaded squares.

⅔

⅓

³⁄₃

⅔

Shade the squares to show the fractions.

⅓

⅔

⅔

³⁄₃

Answers may vary

# Thirds of shapes

Write the fractions for the shaded shapes.

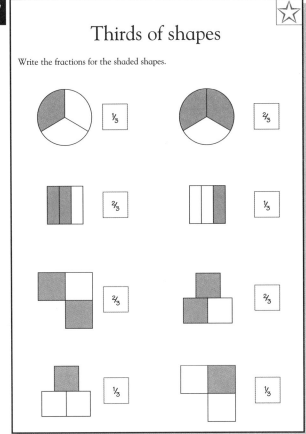

# Fifths

When you divide something into fifths, you share it equally between five.

Each part, or fraction, is called one fifth.
You can also write it as ⅕.

Two parts are two fifths or ⅖.
Three parts are three fifths or ⅗, and so on.

Write the fractions for the shaded squares.

Shade the squares to show the fractions.

*Answers may vary*

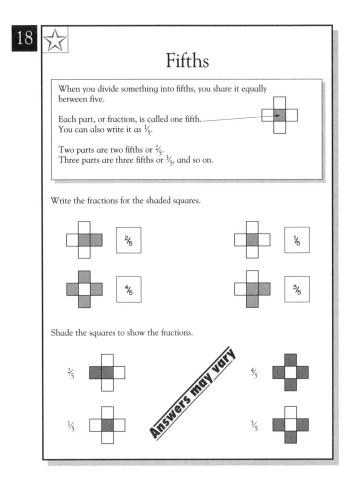

# Fifths of shapes

Write the fractions for the shaded shapes.

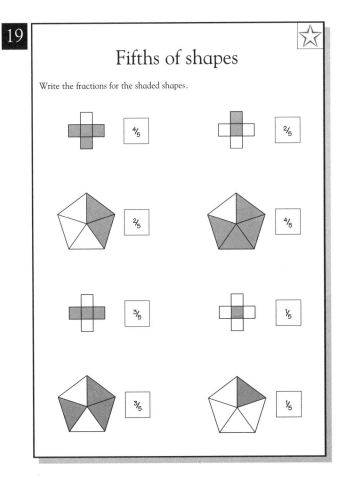

# Tenths

When you divide something into tenths, you share it equally between ten.

Each part, or fraction, is called one tenth.
You can also write it as 1/10.

Two parts are two tenths or 2/10.
Three parts are three tenths or 3/10, and so on.

Write the fractions for the shaded squares.

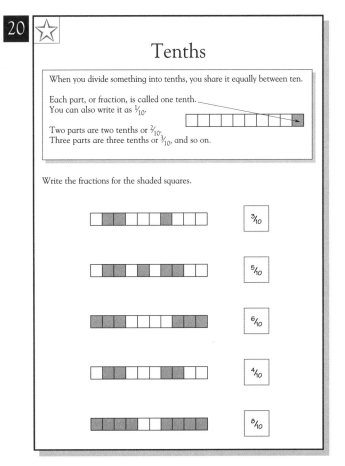

## 21

# Fractions of shapes

Shade these shapes to show the fractions.

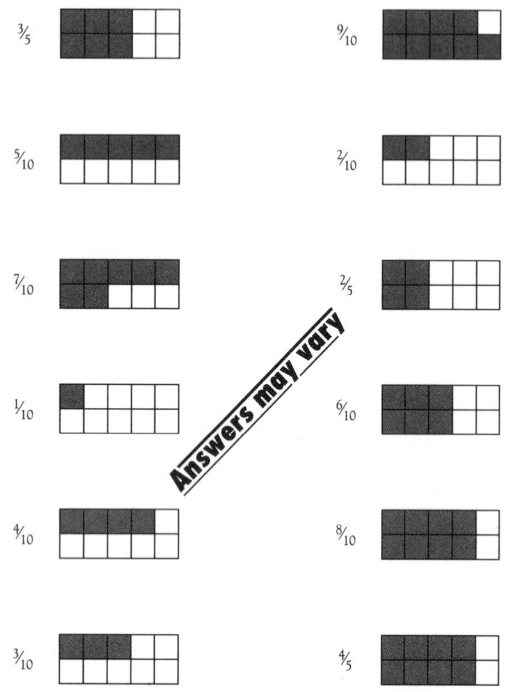
3/5
9/10
5/10
2/10
7/10
2/5
1/10
6/10
4/10
8/10
3/10
4/5
Answers may vary

## 22

# Fraction equivalents

Here are six strips of paper. They are all the same length. Each one has been cut into different fractions. You can see that some fractions are the same. For example, $\frac{1}{2}$ is the same as $\frac{2}{4}$.

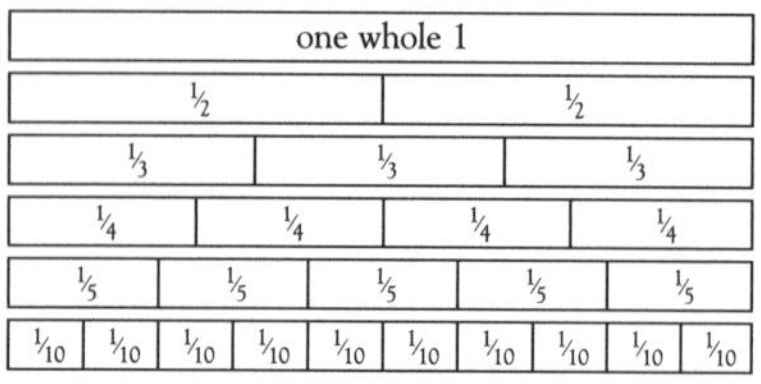
one whole 1
1/2 1/2
1/3 1/3 1/3
1/4 1/4 1/4 1/4
1/5 1/5 1/5 1/5 1/5
1/10 1/10 1/10 1/10 1/10 1/10 1/10 1/10 1/10 1/10

Look at the strips of paper above. Write the fractions that match.

1 is the same as $\frac{4}{4}$

$\frac{4}{10}$ is the same as $\frac{2}{5}$

$\frac{1}{5}$ is the same as $\frac{2}{10}$

$\frac{4}{5}$ is the same as $\frac{8}{10}$

$\frac{2}{5}$ is the same as $\frac{4}{10}$

$\frac{2}{4}$ is the same as $\frac{1}{2}$

$\frac{6}{10}$ is the same as $\frac{3}{5}$

$\frac{8}{10}$ is the same as $\frac{4}{5}$

## 23

# Comparing fractions

You can compare fractions using signs.

< is the sign for *is less than.*
= is the sign for *equals.*
> is the sign for *is greater than.*

Compare the shaded fractions of these blocks. Write < or = or >.

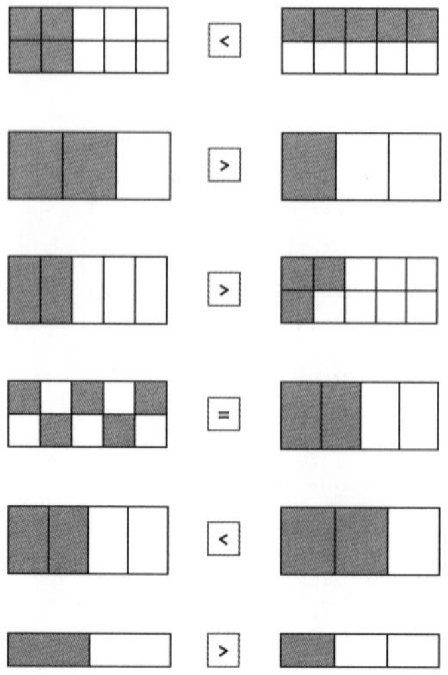
<
>
>
=
<
>

## 24

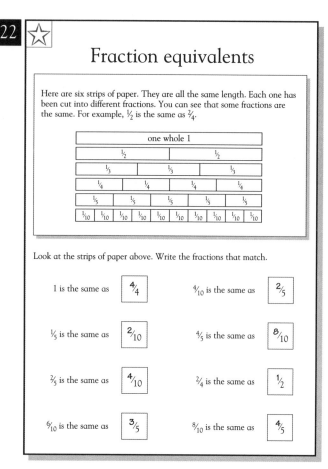

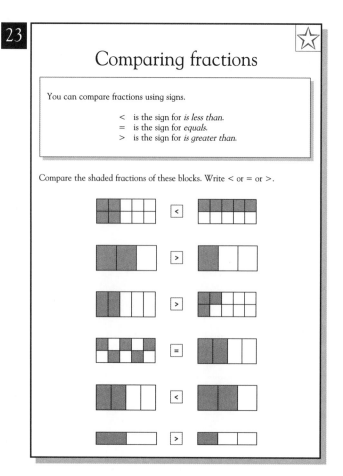

# Sixths

When you divide something into sixths, you share it equally between six.

Each part, or fraction, is called one sixth.
You can also write it as $\frac{1}{6}$.

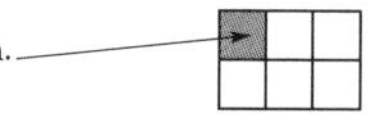

Two parts are two sixths or $\frac{2}{6}$.
Three parts are three sixths or $\frac{3}{6}$, and so on.

Write the fractions for the shaded squares.

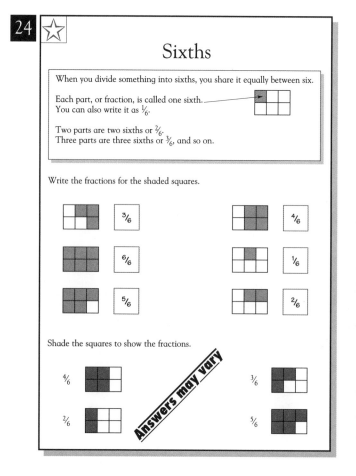

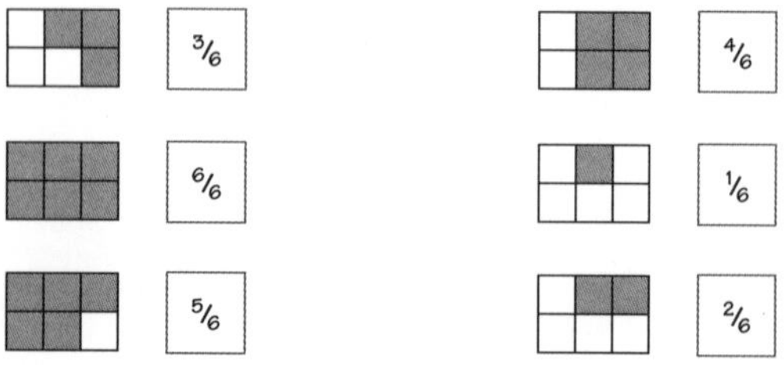
3/6
4/6
6/6
1/6
5/6
2/6

Shade the squares to show the fractions.

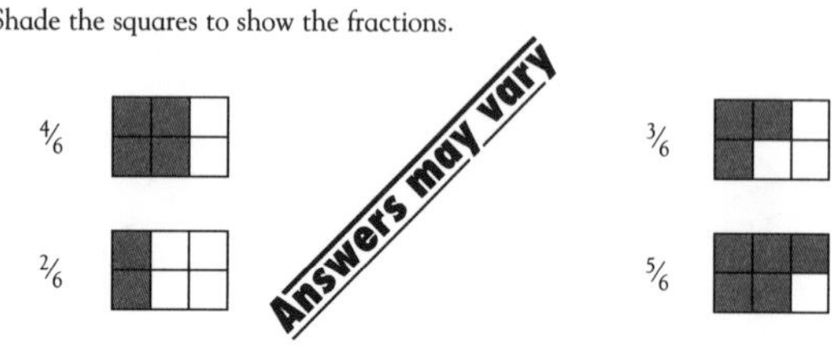
4/6
3/6
2/6
5/6
Answers may vary

25

# Fraction equivalents

Here are six strips of paper. They are all the same length.
Each one has been cut into different fractions. You can see that some fractions are the same. For example, $\frac{1}{2}$ is the same as $\frac{5}{10}$.

| one whole 1 | | | | | | | | | |
|---|---|---|---|---|---|---|---|---|---|
| $\frac{1}{2}$ | $\frac{1}{2}$ | | | | | | | | |
| $\frac{1}{3}$ | $\frac{1}{3}$ | $\frac{1}{3}$ | | | | | | | |
| $\frac{1}{6}$ | $\frac{1}{6}$ | $\frac{1}{6}$ | $\frac{1}{6}$ | $\frac{1}{6}$ | $\frac{1}{6}$ | | | | |
| $\frac{1}{5}$ | $\frac{1}{5}$ | $\frac{1}{5}$ | $\frac{1}{5}$ | $\frac{1}{5}$ | | | | | |
| $\frac{1}{10}$ | $\frac{1}{10}$ | $\frac{1}{10}$ | $\frac{1}{10}$ | $\frac{1}{10}$ | $\frac{1}{10}$ | $\frac{1}{10}$ | $\frac{1}{10}$ | $\frac{1}{10}$ | $\frac{1}{10}$ |

Look at the strips of paper above. Write the fractions that match.

$\frac{4}{5}$ is the same as $\frac{8}{10}$ $\qquad$ $\frac{6}{10}$ is the same as $\frac{3}{5}$

$\frac{4}{10}$ is the same as $\frac{2}{5}$ $\qquad$ $\frac{2}{5}$ is the same as $\frac{4}{10}$

$\frac{2}{3}$ is the same as $\frac{4}{6}$ $\qquad$ $\frac{3}{5}$ is the same as $\frac{6}{10}$

$\frac{1}{5}$ is the same as $\frac{2}{10}$ $\qquad$ $\frac{1}{3}$ is the same as $\frac{2}{6}$

26

# Eighths

When you divide something into eighths, you share it equally between eight.

Each part, or fraction, is called one eighth.
You can also write it as $\frac{1}{8}$.

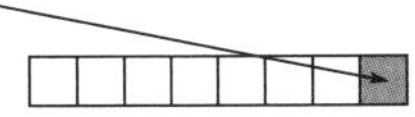

Two parts are two eighths or $\frac{2}{8}$.
Three parts are three eighths or $\frac{3}{8}$, and so on.

Write the fractions for the shaded squares.

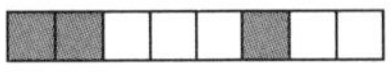 $\frac{3}{8}$

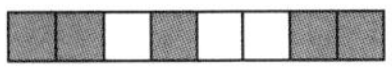 $\frac{5}{8}$

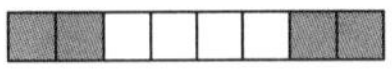 $\frac{4}{8}$

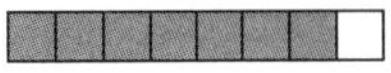 $\frac{7}{8}$

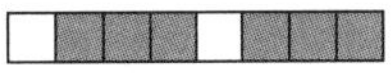 $\frac{6}{8}$

27

# Fraction equivalents

Here are four strips of paper. They are all the same length. Each one has been cut into different fractions. You can see that some fractions are the same. For example, $\frac{1}{2}$ is the same as $\frac{2}{4}$.

| one whole 1 | | | | | | | |
|---|---|---|---|---|---|---|---|
| $\frac{1}{2}$ | $\frac{1}{2}$ | | | | | | |
| $\frac{1}{4}$ | $\frac{1}{4}$ | $\frac{1}{4}$ | $\frac{1}{4}$ | | | | |
| $\frac{1}{8}$ | $\frac{1}{8}$ | $\frac{1}{8}$ | $\frac{1}{8}$ | $\frac{1}{8}$ | $\frac{1}{8}$ | $\frac{1}{8}$ | $\frac{1}{8}$ |

Look at the strips of paper above. Write the fractions that match.

$\frac{1}{2}$ is the same as $\frac{2}{4}$ $\qquad$ $\frac{1}{4}$ is the same as $\frac{2}{8}$

$\frac{1}{2}$ is the same as $\frac{4}{8}$ $\qquad$ $\frac{6}{8}$ is the same as $\frac{3}{4}$

$\frac{2}{4}$ is the same as $\frac{4}{8}$ $\qquad$ $\frac{2}{4}$ is the same as $\frac{1}{2}$

$\frac{2}{8}$ is the same as $\frac{1}{4}$ $\qquad$ $\frac{3}{4}$ is the same as $\frac{6}{8}$

$\frac{4}{8}$ is the same as $\frac{1}{2}$ $\qquad$ $\frac{8}{8}$ is the same as $\frac{2}{2}$

28

# Making one from fractions

If you have one half, you need another half to make one whole 1.

$$\frac{1}{2} + \frac{1}{2} = 1$$

| $\frac{1}{2}$ | $\frac{1}{2}$ |
|---|---|
| one whole 1 | |

Write the fractions you need to make one whole 1.

| | | | | | | | | | | |
|---|---|---|---|---|---|---|---|---|---|---|
| $\frac{1}{3}$ | $\frac{1}{3}$ | $\frac{1}{3}$ | | | | | | | | = 1 |
| $\frac{1}{10}$ | $\frac{1}{10}$ | $\frac{1}{10}$ | $\frac{1}{10}$ | $\frac{1}{10}$ | $\frac{1}{10}$ | $\frac{1}{10}$ | $\frac{1}{10}$ | $\frac{1}{10}$ | $\frac{1}{10}$ | = 1 |
| $\frac{1}{5}$ | $\frac{1}{5}$ | $\frac{1}{5}$ | $\frac{1}{5}$ | $\frac{1}{5}$ | | | | | | = 1 |
| $\frac{1}{6}$ | $\frac{1}{6}$ | $\frac{1}{6}$ | $\frac{1}{6}$ | $\frac{1}{6}$ | $\frac{1}{6}$ | | | | | = 1 |
| $\frac{1}{3}$ | $\frac{2}{3}$ | | | | | | | | | = 1 |
| $\frac{1}{4}$ | $\frac{3}{4}$ | | | | | | | | | = 1 |

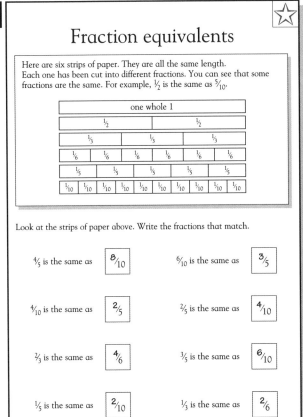

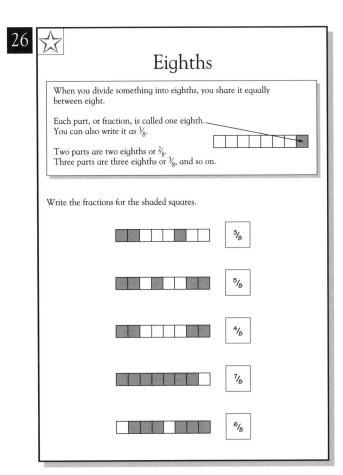

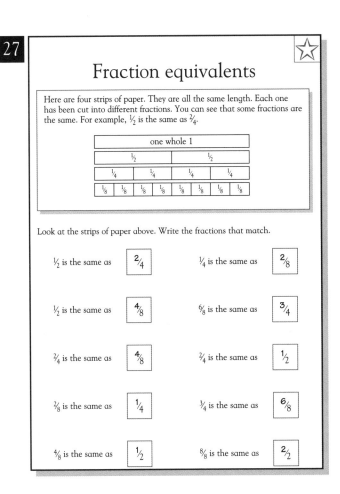

# Making one from fractions

If you have three quarters, you need another quarter to make one whole 1.

$$\frac{3}{4} + \frac{1}{4} = 1$$

| $\frac{3}{4}$ | $\frac{1}{4}$ |
|---|---|
| one whole 1 | |

Write the fractions you need to make one whole 1.

| $\frac{1}{3}$ | $\frac{2}{3}$ | = 1 |

| $\frac{1}{10}$ | $\frac{1}{10}$ | $\frac{1}{10}$ | $\frac{1}{10}$ | $\frac{1}{10}$ | $\frac{1}{10}$ | $\frac{4}{10}$ or $\frac{2}{5}$ | = 1 |

| $\frac{1}{5}$ | $\frac{1}{5}$ | $\frac{3}{5}$ | = 1 |

| $\frac{1}{6}$ | $\frac{1}{6}$ | $\frac{1}{6}$ | $\frac{1}{6}$ | $\frac{2}{6}$ or $\frac{1}{3}$ | = 1 |

| $\frac{1}{3}$ | $\frac{1}{3}$ | $\frac{1}{3}$ | = 1 |

---

# Fractions of shapes

Shade these shapes to show the fractions.

$\frac{2}{5}$    $\frac{3}{4}$

$\frac{2}{3}$    $\frac{1}{2}$

Answers may vary

$\frac{5}{8}$   $\frac{3}{5}$

$\frac{5}{6}$   $\frac{1}{8}$

---

# Fractions of shapes

Shade these shapes to show the fractions.

$\frac{3}{5}$    $\frac{1}{4}$

$\frac{1}{3}$    $\frac{6}{8}$

Answers may vary

$\frac{3}{8}$    $\frac{2}{5}$

$\frac{4}{6}$    $\frac{7}{8}$

---

# Comparing fractions

You can compare fractions using signs.

> is the sign for *is greater than*.
< is the sign for *is less than*.

Here are six strips of paper showing decreasing fractions.

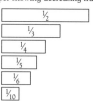

| $\frac{1}{2}$ |
| $\frac{1}{3}$ |
| $\frac{1}{4}$ |
| $\frac{1}{5}$ |
| $\frac{1}{6}$ |
| $\frac{1}{10}$ |

Look at the strips of paper above. Compare the fractions using > or <.

$\frac{1}{2}$ [ > ] $\frac{1}{4}$     $\frac{1}{6}$ [ < ] $\frac{1}{3}$

$\frac{1}{10}$ [ < ] $\frac{1}{5}$     $\frac{1}{4}$ [ < ] $\frac{1}{2}$

$\frac{1}{6}$ [ > ] $\frac{1}{10}$     $\frac{1}{5}$ [ > ] $\frac{1}{6}$

$\frac{1}{5}$ [ < ] $\frac{1}{3}$     $\frac{1}{4}$ [ > ] $\frac{1}{10}$

$\frac{1}{4}$ [ < ] $\frac{1}{3}$     $\frac{1}{3}$ [ < ] $\frac{1}{2}$

# Thirds of shapes

Write the fractions for the shaded shapes.

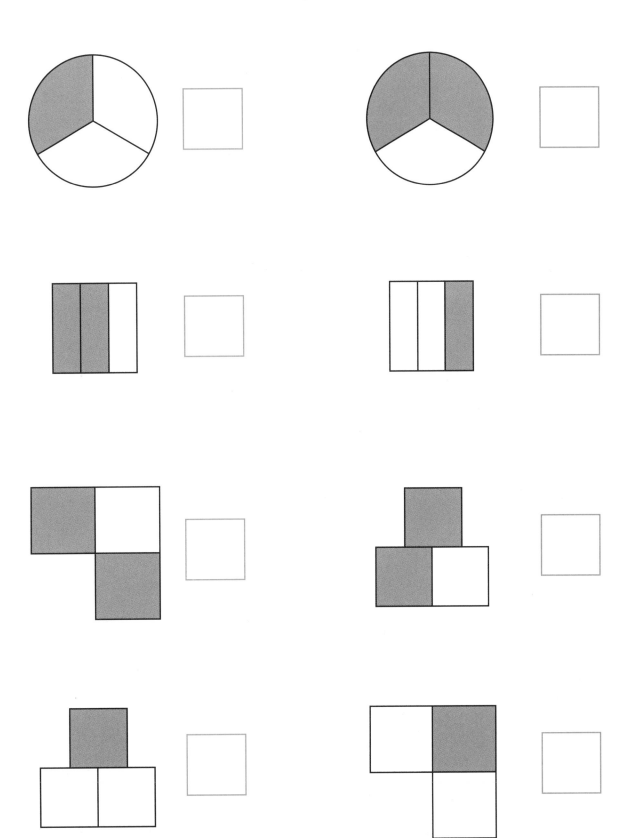

# Fifths

When you divide something into fifths, you share it equally between five.

Each part, or fraction, is called one fifth. You can also write it as $\frac{1}{5}$.

Two parts are two fifths or $\frac{2}{5}$.
Three parts are three fifths or $\frac{3}{5}$, and so on.

Write the fractions for the shaded squares.

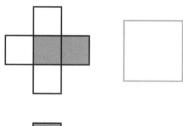

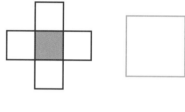

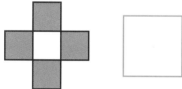

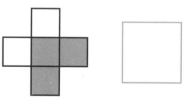

Shade the squares to show the fractions.

$\frac{2}{5}$

$\frac{4}{5}$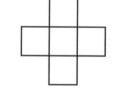

$\frac{1}{5}$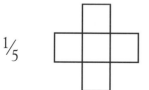

$\frac{3}{5}$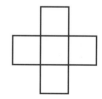

# Fifths of shapes

Write the fractions for the shaded shapes.

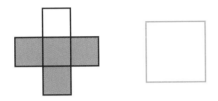

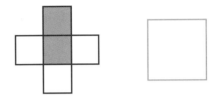

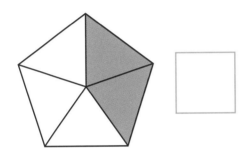

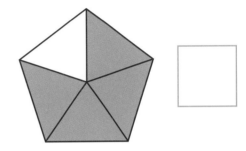

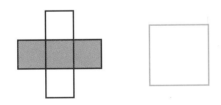

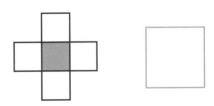

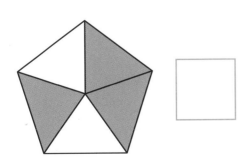

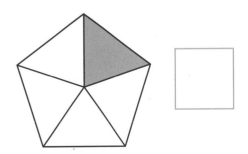

# Tenths

When you divide something into tenths, you share it equally between ten.

Each part, or fraction, is called one tenth.
You can also write it as $\frac{1}{10}$.

Two parts are two tenths or $\frac{2}{10}$.
Three parts are three tenths or $\frac{3}{10}$, and so on.

Write the fractions for the shaded squares.

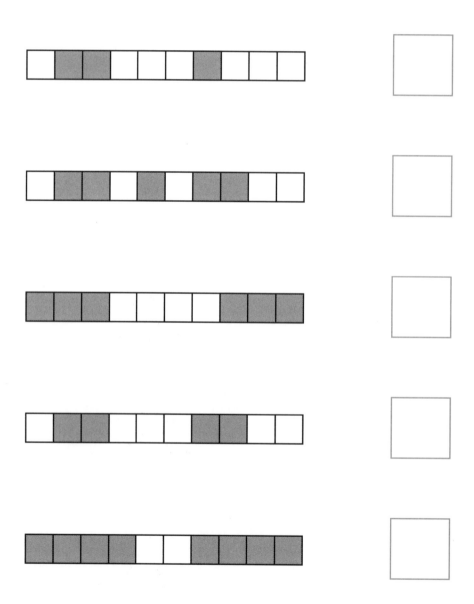

# Fractions of shapes

Shade these shapes to show the fractions.

³⁄₅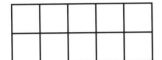

⁹⁄₁₀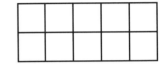

⁵⁄₁₀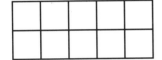

²⁄₁₀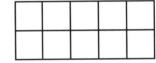

⁷⁄₁₀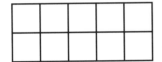

²⁄₅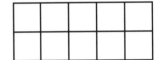

¹⁄₁₀

⁶⁄₁₀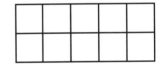

⁴⁄₁₀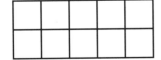

⁸⁄₁₀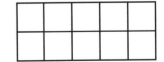

³⁄₁₀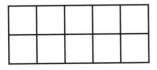

⁴⁄₅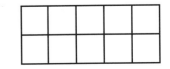

# Fraction equivalents

Here are six strips of paper. They are all the same length. Each one has been cut into different fractions. You can see that some fractions are the same. For example, ½ is the same as ²/₄.

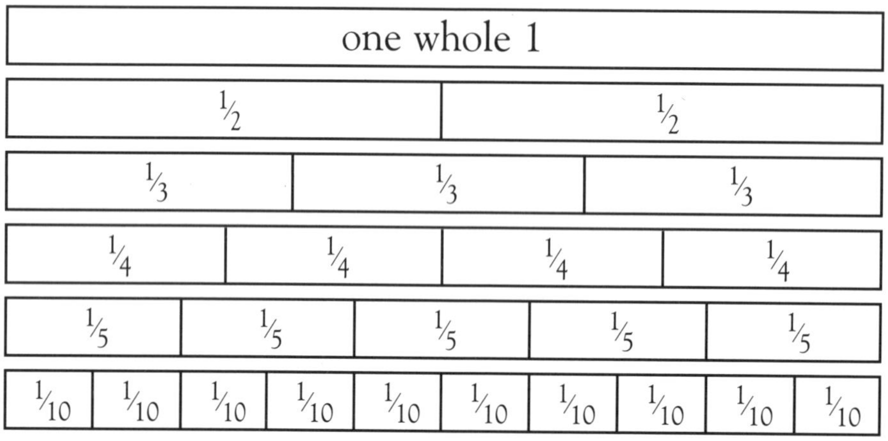

| one whole 1 | | | | | | | | | |
|---|---|---|---|---|---|---|---|---|---|
| ½ | | | | | ½ | | | | |
| ⅓ | | | ⅓ | | | ⅓ | | | |
| ¼ | | ¼ | | ¼ | | | ¼ | | |
| ⅕ | | ⅕ | | ⅕ | | ⅕ | | ⅕ | |
| ¹/₁₀ | ¹/₁₀ | ¹/₁₀ | ¹/₁₀ | ¹/₁₀ | ¹/₁₀ | ¹/₁₀ | ¹/₁₀ | ¹/₁₀ | ¹/₁₀ |

Look at the strips of paper above. Write the fractions that match.

1 is the same as ☐ /4        ⁴/₁₀ is the same as ☐ /5

⅕ is the same as ☐ /10       ⅘ is the same as ☐ /10

⅖ is the same as ☐ /10       ²/₄ is the same as ☐ /2

⁶/₁₀ is the same as ☐ /5      ⁸/₁₀ is the same as ☐ /5

# Comparing fractions

You can compare fractions using signs.

        <    is the sign for *is less than.*
        =    is the sign for *equals.*
        >    is the sign for *is greater than.*

Compare the shaded fractions of these blocks. Write < or = or >.

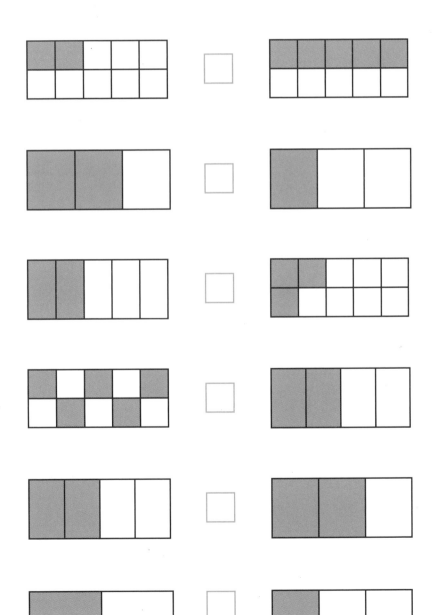

# Sixths

When you divide something into sixths, you share it equally between six.

Each part, or fraction, is called one sixth.
You can also write it as $\frac{1}{6}$.

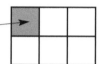

Two parts are two sixths or $\frac{2}{6}$.
Three parts are three sixths or $\frac{3}{6}$, and so on.

Write the fractions for the shaded squares.

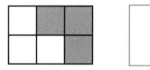

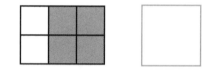

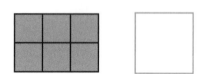

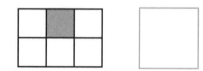

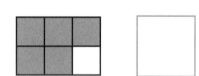

Shade the squares to show the fractions.

$\frac{4}{6}$

$\frac{2}{6}$

$\frac{3}{6}$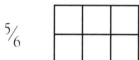

$\frac{5}{6}$

# Fraction equivalents

Here are six strips of paper. They are all the same length.
Each one has been cut into different fractions. You can see that some fractions are the same. For example, ½ is the same as ⁵⁄₁₀.

| one whole 1 | | | | | | | | | |
|---|---|---|---|---|---|---|---|---|---|
| ½ | | | | | ½ | | | | |
| ⅓ | | | ⅓ | | | ⅓ | | | |
| ⅙ | | ⅙ | | ⅙ | | ⅙ | | ⅙ | ⅙ |
| ⅕ | | ⅕ | | ⅕ | | ⅕ | | ⅕ | |
| ¹⁄₁₀ | ¹⁄₁₀ | ¹⁄₁₀ | ¹⁄₁₀ | ¹⁄₁₀ | ¹⁄₁₀ | ¹⁄₁₀ | ¹⁄₁₀ | ¹⁄₁₀ | ¹⁄₁₀ |

Look at the strips of paper above. Write the fractions that match.

⁴⁄₅ is the same as ⬜ /10          ⁶⁄₁₀ is the same as ⬜ /5

⁴⁄₁₀ is the same as ⬜ /5          ²⁄₅ is the same as ⬜ /10

⅔ is the same as ⬜ /6          ³⁄₅ is the same as ⬜ /10

⅕ is the same as ⬜ /10          ⅓ is the same as ⬜ /6

# Eighths

When you divide something into eighths, you share it equally between eight.

Each part, or fraction, is called one eighth.
You can also write it as ⅛.

Two parts are two eighths or ⅜.
Three parts are three eighths or ⅜, and so on.

Write the fractions for the shaded squares.

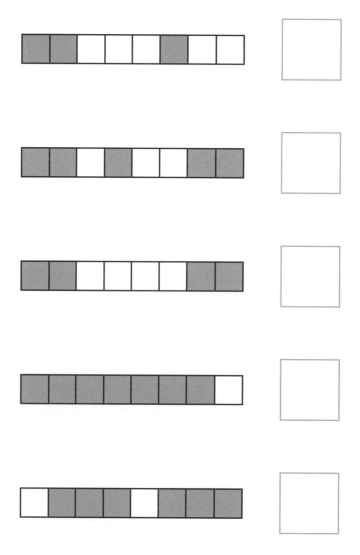

# Fraction equivalents

Here are four strips of paper. They are all the same length. Each one has been cut into different fractions. You can see that some fractions are the same. For example, ½ is the same as ²⁄₄.

| one whole 1 | | | | | | | |
|---|---|---|---|---|---|---|---|
| ½ | | | | ½ | | | |
| ¼ | | ¼ | | ¼ | | ¼ | |
| ⅛ | ⅛ | ⅛ | ⅛ | ⅛ | ⅛ | ⅛ | ⅛ |

Look at the strips of paper above. Write the fractions that match.

½ is the same as ▢ /4          ¼ is the same as ▢ /8

½ is the same as ▢ /8          ⁶⁄₈ is the same as ▢ /4

²⁄₄ is the same as ▢ /8          ²⁄₄ is the same as ▢ /2

²⁄₈ is the same as ▢ /4          ¾ is the same as ▢ /8

⁴⁄₈ is the same as ▢ /2          ⁸⁄₈ is the same as ▢ /2

# Making one from fractions

If you have one half, you need another half to make one whole 1.

½ + ½ = 1

| ½ | ½ |
|:---:|:---:|
| one whole 1 ||

Write the fractions you need to make one whole 1.

| ⅓ | ⅓ | |
|:---:|:---:|:---:|

= 1

| ¹⁄₁₀ | ¹⁄₁₀ | ¹⁄₁₀ | ¹⁄₁₀ | ¹⁄₁₀ | ¹⁄₁₀ | ¹⁄₁₀ | ¹⁄₁₀ | ¹⁄₁₀ | |
|:---:|:---:|:---:|:---:|:---:|:---:|:---:|:---:|:---:|:---:|

= 1

| ⅕ | ⅕ | ⅕ | ⅕ | |
|:---:|:---:|:---:|:---:|:---:|

= 1

| ⅙ | ⅙ | ⅙ | ⅙ | ⅙ | |
|:---:|:---:|:---:|:---:|:---:|:---:|

= 1

| ⅓ | |
|:---:|:---:|

= 1

| ¼ | |
|:---:|:---:|

= 1

# Making one from fractions

If you have three quarters, you need another quarter to make one whole 1.

$$\tfrac{3}{4} + \tfrac{1}{4} = 1$$

| $\tfrac{3}{4}$ | $\tfrac{1}{4}$ |
|---|---|
| one whole 1 | |

Write the fractions you need to make one whole 1.

| $\tfrac{1}{3}$ | |
|---|---|

= 1

| $\tfrac{1}{10}$ | $\tfrac{1}{10}$ | $\tfrac{1}{10}$ | $\tfrac{1}{10}$ | $\tfrac{1}{10}$ | $\tfrac{1}{10}$ | |
|---|---|---|---|---|---|---|

= 1

| $\tfrac{1}{5}$ | $\tfrac{1}{5}$ | |
|---|---|---|

= 1

| $\tfrac{1}{6}$ | $\tfrac{1}{6}$ | $\tfrac{1}{6}$ | $\tfrac{1}{6}$ | |
|---|---|---|---|---|

= 1

| $\tfrac{1}{3}$ | $\tfrac{1}{3}$ | |
|---|---|---|

= 1

# Fractions of shapes

Shade these shapes to show the fractions.

²⁄₅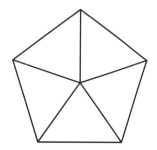

³⁄₄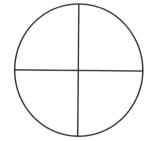

²⁄₃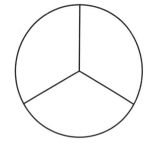

½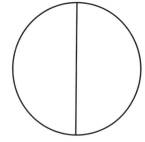

⅝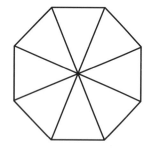

³⁄₅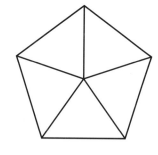

⅚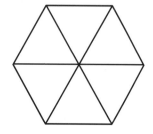

⅛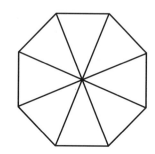

# Fractions of shapes

Shade these shapes to show the fractions.

$\frac{3}{5}$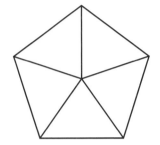

$\frac{1}{4}$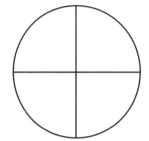

$\frac{1}{3}$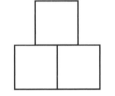

$\frac{6}{8}$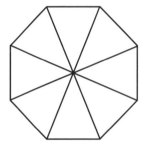

$\frac{3}{8}$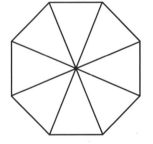

$\frac{2}{5}$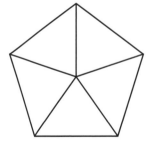

$\frac{4}{6}$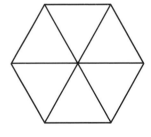

$\frac{7}{8}$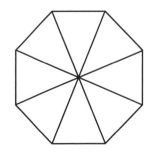

# Comparing fractions

You can compare fractions using signs.

> is the sign for *is greater than*.
< is the sign for *is less than*.

Here are six strips of paper showing decreasing fractions.

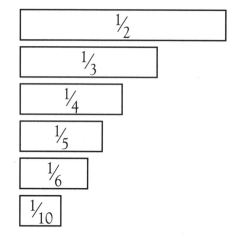

Look at the strips of paper above. Compare the fractions using > or <.

½ ☐ ¼          ⅙ ☐ ⅓

¹⁄₁₀ ☐ ⅕          ¼ ☐ ½

⅙ ☐ ¹⁄₁₀          ⅕ ☐ ⅙

⅕ ☐ ⅓          ¼ ☐ ¹⁄₁₀

¼ ☐ ⅓          ⅓ ☐ ½